The Journey

A breast cancer patient's courageous story
in verse and prose
of the physical and mental challenges
of getting well again

by Bernice Glavin

Published with the support of the
Cork Cancer Research Centre at
the Mercy University Hospital
and University College Cork.
All proceeds from the sale of this book
will be donated to the Centre

www.ccrc.ie
Registered Charity No. CHY 11831

i

The Journey.
Published by Elmvale Books, Wilton, Cork, Ireland.

ISBN 978-0-9554846-0-5

Published with the assistance of Cork Cancer Research, Cork, Ireland.

Printed and bound by Lee Press Ltd, South Terrace, Cork City, Ireland.

CONTENTS

About the Author

Bernice Glavin is from Wilton in Cork City. She is a nurse who has spent most of her life working in an Intensive Care Unit. While the inspiration for this book came from her own experiences as a cancer patient, her writing also reflects her close observation of people and sharing the trauma in the daily lives of others.

She describes herself as a "water and road" person being a regular swimmer and marathon runner.

Bernice began writing poetry in her early teens but pursued it more avidly over the past few years. Her topics range from simple every day occurrences to an appreciation of nature, the search for contentment and occasional imaginary situations.

In every poem there is a theme to which somebody can relate. Sadness and joy, yes, but also humour and common sense.

This selection of poems is primarily developed around the subject of cancer and draws from her own experiences from the shock of diagnosis through to the joy of growing reassurance and the new vision of the future ahead. Hopefully, other cancer patients will relate to the themes and ideas and realise that life can really begin when the gloomy days are put behind.

The verses will make you sigh and smile, in turn. Many people will instantly relate to Bernice's remarkable insights. For others, the poems will, hopefully, help to take fear out of the cancer word and ease the mystery and uncertainty of cancer treatment.

The poems empower the reader to challenge their own problems and in doing so will be drawn back again and again to reading the book.

DEDICATION

This book is humbly dedicated
to all women and men
who have to take on
The Journey
from cancer diagnosis
to the end of treatment and to the
skilled and wonderful hospital people
who keep them focused on the triumph
that lies ahead.

I wish to acknowledge the support
and encouragement from my daughter Kate,
my parents, Dick and Cassie,
my sisters, Anne, Colette and Fiona,
their husbands and children
and my loyal friends who always believed
I could write this book.

My special thanks, too, to Mr. Denis Richardson,
Dr. Seamus O'Reilly, Dr. Seamus O'Cathail,
Dr. Garry Lee, Dr. Joan Fitzgerald and team,
along with the staff of the Morris Corridor;
the Breast Unit and the Oncology Unit
and the Physiotherapy Department
at the South Infirmary/Victoria Hospital, Cork,
and the staff of the Radiotherapy Department
at Cork University Hospital.

I particularly thank Professor Gerry O'Sullivan,
Surgeon and Director–in-Chief
of the Cork Cancer Research Centre
and its General Manager, Dr Declan Soden
for so willingly adopting this book
as a fund-raising project.

The Journey

Cancer is a word that instils fear in most people. It is a condition that will touch most families throughout a lifetime. My own family is one of them.
The initial suggestion that I might have cancer was one I could not even begin to entertain. I was in total denial having run the Dublin City Marathon only a week earlier and in a good time. I felt it was not even remotely possible. I also felt I looked too healthy to have cancer.

I was in a state of total shock and disbelief. As I saw it there were people out there really sick but I was not one of them. But the inevitable happened. An edgy restless and mounting panic took over the back of my mind. I also felt that all the medical people simply covered all possible eventualities and this made me suspicious that they were preparing me for the shock that, deep down, I knew was coming my way.

In those early days I may have appeared normal on the outside but, under the surface, there was total despair and emptiness. My daily existence passed in a blur and I was numb and disconnected from the reality of life. I pretended to be fine but I was far from fine. In fact, I could have burst open with grief and emotion.

Again and again I asked the question everyone asks. "Why me?" And, of course, there was no answer. I could have screamed out loud and yet I didn't want to cause a commotion. Now I look back and wonder if people could, at the time, sense my inner turmoil.

As I write this, I have gone through all the twin treatments of radiotherapy and chemotherapy and the physical and emotional upheavals that go with them. The hair piece - abandoned anyway because of the excessive summer heat – and the bandana have themselves taken a long journey and Bernice's hair is self-restoring and looking good.

This little book of poems and the stories of how they came about attempts to convey some of the multitude of different feelings that confronted me on my journey. I honestly find it difficult to tell my story in this public way but my wish is that it will bring understanding, hope and certainty to people who also have to ask the same question: "Why me?" and to all people who, for whatever reason, think that, for them, the sun will never shine again.

- BERNICE

The Diagnosis

An endless wait
leads to bad news,
more consultations.
How could this happen to me?
Why?

People look
and attempt to conceal
the pity that shows
in their eyes,
glad its not them.

My mind,
frantic and numb with shock,
does not function
or comprehend simple things.
It has shut down.

My body is trembling;
My life flashes before me.
There are so many things
I have left
undone!

Consoling words of
'You'll be fine',
'You look so well',
are uttered falteringly,
knowing this may not be so.

Who selected me
as the person for this?
There are people out there
far more deserving than I.
Why me?

.

While I waited for the results I suddenly noticed things more vividly than before. I had always appreciated life and good health. Any day I was out in the fresh air was a good day to me regardless of the weather and I had felt lucky to be alive.

But sometimes an uneasy feeling made me wonder if it could all change sometime and now, it seemed, that moment had come.

This poem describes how I'd always felt and then how I valued those feelings even more as the days of waiting for my diagnosis slowly dragged along.

At Times Like This

When the winter sunshine weakly shines

You appreciate life's happy times.

When a card drops unexpectedly through your door

You feel much better than before.

When the phone shrills on the silent day

A friend's voice brightens up your way;

A stranger's smile on a busy street

Shows all the good in the folk you meet.

When a fellow driver waves you through

It lightens the tension in the traffic queue.

When a dog bounds up, giving his tail a wag

Your spirits lift and no longer sag.

On days like this a kindly thought

Brightens your existence, as it ought,

Opening up a beam of light,

Making everything seem bright.

My big regret at this time was that I had spent
most of my life worrying about daily events
that were really only minor incidents when put
into perspective.

One of my earlier poems "What If?" was my
attempt to show this. Looking back, my whole
life had consisted of lists and deadlines.

Now, I wondered what I had missed along the
way while I was constantly trying to save the
whole world when I should have stood back
and let the world take care of itself.

This poem tries to convey my thoughts
on the subject.

The True Meaning of Life

The rat race
of life
is irrelevant.
In one split second
it may end,
be over
never to come back.

Previously idyllic times
might suddenly stop,
leaving a gulf
so wide
that nothing
will cause it
to be closed.

Every moment
of every day
is precious,
treasured,
a one-off experience;
immeasurable
in monetary terms.

Worry and anxiety
are useless;
a waste
of valuable space
and time.
Better to be an opportunity
where positive things are achieved.

A rainy day
is not a bad day
but a bump on your horizon.
Rainy days
cause flowers to grow
and simply prove
that life goes on.

This poem was written as a response to the visit to my GP and I credit her with saving me.

Three days after my daughter and I made the agonising decision to put our beloved elderly and sick dog to sleep I attended the GP on a routine matter.

As I was leaving the surgery I mentioned a mark on my skin and from that moment my life was altered forever.

The poet Seamus Heaney would refer to a serious illness as a door into the dark and that is how it initially appeared to me.

Pause Awhile

An occasional
ache
is not a bad thing.
It is there
to remind us
to listen more
to ourselves.

Our body
functions effortlessly,
now and again
telling us
that it's tired,
overused,
due to our inability to rest.

Do not ignore it.
Thank it
for taking the time
to tell you
to slow down
in a world where deadlines
are excessive.

You cannot reach
that goal
without your body's help.
It works tirelessly,
complaining only when
pushed to the limit
and it can't go on.

Step back for a while.
Recall the last time
you did nothing.
It may not be possible
to remember.
This time might be
the first.

On your birthday
treat yourself!
Congratulate your body
on a job well done,
offering
Best Wishes
for the Year to Come.

One day while I was in hospital I watched the movement of visitors. Some ambled along. Others rushed as if trying to get the last seat for the big show.

Everybody seemed so solemn and yet I envied their freedom – and their appearance of well-being.

I wondered if everybody was too busy to even notice me or notice any other patient whose trauma was equally private and personal and, perhaps, overwhelming.

The Lift

Patient seeks the lift as doors fling wide,

Rushing visitors pour out from inside,

Scurrying to get on with their busy day,

Oblivious to the patient and her dismay.

Patient wonders: 'Do they even see my face?

'Do they consider my existence outside this place?

'Apart from their own reason to make the call

'Do they even notice the posters on the wall?'

Patient ambles, just using time,

Willing that soon all will be fine.

People rushing to and fro

Not seeing the patient as they go.

Patient seeks the lift as doors fling wide,

Rushing visitors pour out from inside,

Scurrying to get on with their busy day,

Oblivious to the patient and her dismay.

It can be difficult to sleep in hospital. That is the experience of most people, especially in the early nights when the surroundings seem so different to that at home.

For me, it was probably a combination of anxiety, the different environment, the routine and timetable. Prior to this I would have been a creature of habit.

I would say that my inability to relax was also a big factor in all of this.

Sleep brings harmony to the body and, without it, we become different people. Suddenly, it's a crisis.

When it is all over and we are back in our own surroundings we can see the humour in it all.

Sleep Deprivation

Tablets taken, I settle down
Covered by sheet and eiderdown,
Preparing for a peaceful night,
Dimmed lights and not too bright.

Two hours pass, time slowly ticks,
'Lie down, relax, it will soon be six'.
More hours and minutes stumble by;
Whoever said that time could fly?

Panic rears its ugly head,
'What if I'm awake all night instead?'
Sheep pass by, two thousand and two,
Deep breaths making me a shade of blue.

My eyes close, I'm starting to dream.
I'm back in time to where I've been,
Co-ordinating an emergency and doing well
But suddenly I wake and I'm back in hell.

The corner chair becomes a joyrider's car
Racing towards me from afar.
I hold my breath 'cause my end has come,
The "car" so close I cannot run.

I slow my breaths and know I'm awake,
It's only a dream for heaven's sake.
My rest forgotten once again,
I might sleep sometime – but I don't know when.

As a nurse myself I felt at home on occasions when I could watch and appreciate the nurses working with a kindness and professionalism that is so important in the hospital environment, especially in the modern era.

Staff shortages, increasing workloads and never-ending paperwork are only some of the extra demands on nurses on a daily basis.

Re-allocation of nurses to different patients on a regular basis is good for building up nursing skills but may be upsetting for a patient who develops a relationship with a particular nurses and feels an added sense of security as a result.

Then again, everybody deals with problems and events in different ways.

Eavesdropping

Sitting by the nurses' station at Report time

I hear interesting words that used to be mine.

Words like "care plan" and "implement"

And "has a referral form been sent?"

"3D needs pre-med, permission's signed."

The notice board shows tasks underlined.

"The post op. is stable and her pressure fine;

"6A's temperature may settle in time".

"4C is fasting for procedure in a.m.,

"5A's surgery is scheduled for ten.

"Shift's nearly over yet there's so much to do,

"We were all so busy that time just flew..."

Anybody who knows me well will be aware that I value my sense of space. Hence, some days I really wanted to get to the hospital door and stand outside to feel the breeze on my face while attempting to get my thoughts together.

I really appreciated it when I was allowed to leave the hospital to spend a day at home before my third visit to Theatre. I was extremely grateful to people who visited and spent time with me but at that moment I was so devastated that I was barely capable of conducting a normal conversation.

This poem conveys my thoughts at the time of turmoil but is in no way intended to offend or reject those great people who went out of their way to visit me or contact me.

The numerous cards I received are now kept in a special box. In the early days, after the "bad" days, I used to take them out and be very cheered at the fact that all these wonderful people remembered me so generously.

I suppose, in practice, as far as any seriously ill patient is concerned, the ideal visitor is the one who thinks of the patient and asks themselves just what would be an appropriate length of visit and intensity of conversation for that particular situation.

Visitors

Will your well-meaning chatter ever cease?

Can you not go now and let me in peace?

Can you not see that I'm screaming inside?

Please have your conversations away outside.

One at a time is not too bad;

Two together could drive you mad,

Conducting debate across my bed

Not realising the turmoil inside my head.

Some are great and don't stay long,

Others need entertaining, maybe a song,

The telephone ringing as you're having a rest,

Is the worst of all - the ultimate test.

Now, visitors are caring and all very kind,

But may dig up memories that I've left behind.

So please, dear visitor think how I feel

And leave me in peace to recover and heal.

I went to Theatre a third time. The third was for mastectomy. On that day I did not know how to feel. I wondered if I should be grieving and saying "goodbye" or trying to put on a brave face which, I knew, would be the right way to do things.

I opted to be tough as I felt the other options were not for me. Deep down I was afraid I might get hysterical and not be able to go through with it.

Looking back now I realise I was grieving over something that was totally out of my control. Yet, I can still vividly recall those feelings as I look back over it all.

This poem tries to convey the anguish I was going through on the day.

Grieving

Showering
for the last time
I cannot
look to see
what soon
will no longer
be mine.

I soap and soap,
looking away,
tortured
that despite the care given
it must end this way.
Four hours left
and no way out.

My mind drifts
attempting
to divert,
trying to ignore
the gravity
of the situation
I am in.

Re-applying the dressing
I try not to look at
or feel
something
that was part of me for so long
and shortly
will be gone..

I wonder
should I say
'goodbye'
or 'good luck'
before
time passes
and it is too late.

But I cannot.
It is all too difficult
and words are not enough.
I try to ignore it,
hoping that tomorrow
I will not be sorry
On finding it is no longer there.

My three trips to theatre and my subsequent visit to the recovery room distressed me for a while afterwards. But I was privileged to meet the most extraordinary team of professionals who were so kind, caring and courteous.

I can still recall the bright lights and all the hustle and bustle that goes on in the aftermath of operations.

I remember answering questions and the answers I gave but I have no memory of the faces behind the questioning voices.

Then I settled down to my own private programme of visions and delusions as the morphine took over.

Morphine and Visions

Recovery room voices
call me,
prompting my hoarse reply
across busy hospital sounds.
Back in my bed
my mind drifts,
thinking.........

I am watering plants,
then sitting on a bench
with an old man ,
a stranger.
Yet, in the warm sunshine
I feel calm
in his presence.

I am lying in bed,
immobile,
wrapped in blankets,
numbed by injections
temporarily relaxed.
The corridor's quiet.
The monitor bleeps.

I smell food
and, in the distance,
doors open.
Nurses scurry about.
Far away
A telephone
rings.

I am relieved
it is over
for now
Whatever will follow
is presently forgotten
Recovery Room memories
fading from my mind.

My morphine induced state
permits me to see
a staring giraffe
standing in the corner
and a joyriding armchair,
along with a scampering mouse
that is not really there.

Reaction varies among people as they approach the day of discharge from hospital, especially after major surgery. For me I had a dreadful fear of the outside world and I worried about the events ahead and wondered, yet again, if life would ever be the same. I also feared I might lose my independence.

Within the hospital other people were responsible for me. The thought that I was now responsible for myself once more filled me with fear and insecurity. Maybe this came from the fact that I had always been independent and a decision-maker.

I felt odd to be without my ID bracelet on my wrist. I missed my team of efficient carers and the domestic staff who so constantly had boosted my morale.

My goal now was to try to break the dependency of the past seventeen days and restore my confidence by developing the ability to boost and encourage myself back to being the person I had been.

Homeward Bound

An initial stay
of three days
brought
three operations,
many needles,
bad news
and tumbling tears.

As I leave
I am afraid
to face
the outside world
terrified
to do the things
I loved.

I've become cocooned,
institutionalised,
unwillingly dependant,
worrying
as I step outside
becoming once again
responsible for myself.

In the initial days and weeks after leaving hospital I had my ups and downs. Sometimes I pretended that everything was wonderful but most of the time I was afraid and was shaking inside.

I was often amazed that my heart could still beat and my whole being still function despite the pressures I was putting on it with my constant fear of the unknown.

My strategy was to think only of the present and to abandon long-term thinking. I had to be patient because, at the beginning, even simple tasks seemed to take much longer.

Eventually I learned to slow down but I never learned to relax and, inevitably, the issue of the future and the need for planning, began to invade the mind.

The next poem is my attempt to show both the positive and negative sides of those days.

Life Goes On

In the end
I survived,
came out
alive,
stronger,
more determined
than before.

Other fences to climb
do not seem as high.
Follow-up treatments
will be conquered.
They are but hurdles
to be jumped
- then left behind!

Life will go on
as before.
Hopefully, I will
worry less
but, knowing myself,
I will be anxious
all the same.

This poem was written on Christmas Day and the mood of it reflects my feelings on the day as I sat up in bed at early morning and pondered a world outside full of laughter and celebration against my own desolation.

But the tears came and went and my self-belief began to edge through like the sun on the evening of a thunderstorm.

Deep down I knew that this terrible moment would never happen in my life again.

I had thought of leaving it out of this published collection and holding it back as a very private poem. But it was real life and this little book is about real life so it is given its place.

Christmas Morning

Christmas morning:
a tear
trickles down
my thinner face.
Sadly, Santa
did not
grant my requests.

Very simply,
I needed
my left breast
back
as before
right there
in it's usual place.

My other wish was
that my dog of
eleven-and-a-half years
would return.
She died
three days
before all this began.

A new dog
will arrive
in a matter
of time
when circumstances
permit
it to be so.

The left-sided space
is there,
ongoing treatments
providing assurance,
preventing
anything like this
ever happening again.

In order to survive in a difficult situation you need to do what is right for you. What may suit one person is not best for another and it is purely a question of individual choice.

Some people get consolation and relief from massage, aromatherapy and counselling.

Right at the beginning a doctor had told me: "When dealing with you we are not dealing with a normal person."
I knew what she was saying. It was a tribute of the nicest possible kind. She understood me as a person.

In the event, I dealt with crises and the like in my own way as the next poem tries to show. I certainly wouldn't advocate running in the rain or a training regime for a person who is ill.

But I had always been super fit and over the years I had run all the major marathons, including Dublin and Belfast.

From the emotional point of view going back on the road so early on was, for me, one of the best things I did.

On the day in question I gained far more than I lost. I took up the challenge – and won.

Winter Blues

January Fifth, a dull old day,

Not bright for me in any way,

So I did something I shouldn't have done,

Running in rain and not in sun.

I could have stayed home, followed the rule,

But I ignored it deciding it was old school,

I took to the road and got soaked through,

Positive thoughts now reduced to a few.

On and on, mile after mile,

Eventually I finished and began to smile,

The day went on tho' bleak and grey,

But my mind was warm, I'd won the day.

The moral of my story is do not give in,

Try what you like, even on a whim,

Life is too short to do everything right,

Face every day with a grin and a fight.

My experience with cancer brought me close to the goodwill and generosity in people. But it is also a fact that many people simply don't know what to say when meeting for the first time somebody who has had cancer.

There were occasions when people actually cried as they held my hand. There were occasions when people avoided me, not knowing what to say or how to say it.

Sometimes I became the consoler rather than the consoled because, strangely, the recovering patient can handle these situations better than the person they meet. All of these are good people and well intentioned.

I was, and still am, overwhelmed at the sheer generosity of spirit and the goodwill that people wrapped around me.

This little poem attempts to seek out the philosophies, even humour, that emerge around the most serious moments.

The Things They Say

'You look far too healthy to have that.'
'You'll lose your hair but get a nice hat.'

'You are fit and strong, it will get you through.'
'You've a year off work – how I envy you!'

'You'll find that things will fall into place.'
'You'll face each day at your own pace.'

'You've the hard part over; God, you're a saint.'
'You know lots of people with the same complaint.'

'You could be killed by a bus as you cross the road.'
'You know the treatment you're on is a heavy load.'

'You are lucky to have something that can be cured.'
'You'd need to make sure you are well insured.'

'You must trust in God that all will be well.'
'You'll get over this… and time will tell!

Each of my poems were written to catch the
mood of a particular day. Some were good but
others were "down" days as the treatment took
its on the constitution and the morale.

My oncology team were wonderful and
repeatedly adjusted my medication, as they do
with all patients, to seek further improvements.

One of the "down" days was the second day of
February and I saw that a local magazine was
looking for a Valentine's Day poem for its poetry
page. Lying on the couch I took up the
challenge!

The poem won the competition and brought a
candlelight dinner for my daughter and myself
on Valentine's Night when I was presented with
a beautiful bouquet of roses.

Our picture appeared on the following week and
the lying camera was kind to the sight of my
thinning hair. I have happy memories of the day.

A Valentine Card

A teenage girl uttered with a sigh:
I need a Valentine Card or I'll cry.
It can show roses, or even mention love,
Push it through my letterbox with a gentle shove.

You do not even have to sign your name,
An X will suffice to ease my pain,
You will make my day with that simple thought
By sending the card that you have bought.

You could describe yourself if you want
And I'd go to school with a card to flaunt!
If you are good-looking it would be great,
But maybe I'm just tempting fate!

If that somebody hears my plea
I'd make a lovely girlfriend you will see.
We could meet for a while on Valentine's Night
And I'd really hope it would turn out right.

I'm not asking for much – just a card or note,
You'd save me showing the one I wrote,
So please, please send it. Send it. Do!
And I'll be forever grateful to you.

This poem was written for a friend of mine when a very dear relative of hers died from an illness other than cancer. I had just started my chemotherapy at the time.

But I thought it might be included as a tribute, as well, to all people with cancer but who were not as lucky as those of us who survived to tell the tale.

Hopefully, in the not-too-distant future, it will be possible to make even earlier cancer diagnoses, have improved screening and, with advances in medication and treatment, fewer good people will leave us to become angels.

For the most part these advances will come from research, here at home and on an international scale and supported by generous people at private, organisational and corporate levels.

The Guardian Angel

A new angel arrived in heaven today,
'I heard', said Peter, 'you were on your way,
'Put this halo above your head
'As a symbol of the good life you have led.

'Do not queue, there is no need,
'Proceed inside, you are welcome indeed.
'We've admired your gentleness and your grace,
'The constant kindness showing in your face.

'Your leaving earth is heaven's gain,
'We're sad for your family and feel their pain.
'They need not despair because up above
'Heaven's new angel will watch with love.

'They will think of you as days go by,
'Miss you, sure, even quietly cry,
'But as a Guardian Angel, we have agreed
'You will always help in their hour of need'

This poem was written in response to the first occasion I had to go "public", so to speak, without the regular long and natural tresses.

The time came to get my head shaved and I began to wear my lovely new hairpiece of similar length to my own. So magnificent a work of art was it that only those who knew me detected anything special. In fact, I was regularly complimented on my hair!

As a keen runner and swimmer I was encountering new difficulties. Apart from evidence of surgery, it's not possible to take a richly textured, full-length hairpiece into a swimming pool. But a little planning and a little daring and courage, saw me through all situations.

Apart from the surgery I would say that the worst experience for me was losing my hair. These verses describe it well but could never express the heartache and the sadness it caused me. My sense of loss was tremendous and would only be shared by others who have had a similar experience.

By now as I write these words, the hair is starting to assert itself again but the insecurity will go on until I have the option of again having that long ponytail swinging in the breeze. The colour or mix of colours remains to be seen. But it never went away. It was only in hiding.

Hair today – Gone Tomorrow

My pride and joy, my lovely hair,
Soon to be no longer there,
Medication and treatments will make it go,
Not a single hair will I have to show.

Hairs drift aimlessly to the floor
I am devastated, it will be no more.
My brush is filled with silky strands,
A downy film drifts along my hands.

My jumper's coated with shades of gold,
My daughter wonders can hair be sold.
On my bedroom floor I see the sheen,
It fell from my head where it's always been.

A solitary hair drifts aimlessly,
Why did this have to happen to me?
I gather some lengths as souvenirs
Of happier days in bygone years.

Later on when my skull looks white,
There's this one thought to bring delight,
When my lovely hair returns once more
It may even be nicer than before.

If sleepless nights were a feature of the hospital stay they were also a fact of life as I settled into home life again. Chemotherapy doesn't help and it is always difficult in the early weeks after breast surgery to find a comfortable sleeping position.

I must have visited every mart and hillside farm searching for sheep to count but I had to adopt a different approach. I concentrated on the nice things and happy events to which I'd treat myself in the months and years after treatment finished.

One vision that rested easily on the mind without being in the slighted way distressful at that hour of night was the future arrival of a new dog. By the time he eventually arrived I already knew him well and the sheep were back grazing happily on the hills unaware of the mathematical havoc they had caused!

Counting Sheep

At last I've given up counting sheep,
I've seen so many I almost weep;
I image a happy dog instead,
My favourite sight is a spaniel's head.

His ears are curly, soft and brown,
He almost smiles and would never frown,
His furry paws are, oh, so sweet,
His wagging tail is plump and neat.

He has no name, at least not yet,
But when he's here I'll call him pet.
Now that I've found a way to sleep,
I've finally given up counting sheep.

Children are wonderful at a time like this. Their awareness of change is only matched by their outspoken honesty. My nieces and nephews and their masterly evaluation of an adult predicament became jewels of wisdom and directness. I will always smile as my mind replays those special moments.

Little girls, aged five to eight, knew all the reasons for hair loss and the need for a woolly hat to keep me warm. It proved that simple, honest answers by a mother to simple, honest questions, is the key to success with little ones.

And the drain from my arm in the early days in hospital was accepted as my new CD attachment.

One of my nephews never gave up asking if my hair had grown yet. It was an almost daily question. The disbelief when he could finally see the evidence of my fresh crop, is a memory worth having.

Nieces and Nephews

With a gentle tap upon my arm
My niece whispered with childish charm,
"We know about your hair", she said,
"And that it's gone from on your head"

I said 'twas tucked beneath my hat!
She said: "Oh mum told us all about that.
"The medicine to make your sore arm good
"Made your hair fall out – mum said it would"

My sister looked with a gentle smile,
My niece assured me: "It will grow in a while,
"Mum told us it would end up ok"
A lttle girl's wisdom, what I could say?

Her two sisters quickly then agreed
That this information was right indeed.
In fact, they told me: "We think you're cool
And our cousins pray for you at school."

Life is never totally full of doom and gloom and that part of my mind given over to serious verse-writing one night took a holiday and gave me a picture of life in a dream world in which the toys took advantage of the adult sleeping hours for a little nursery playtime.

I regularly smile to myself at the whole idea.

People have different ways of getting through their tough times and I would say go for it, if it suits you. Poetry is one of mine. Some people I met go to ballroom dancing. Others knit or play music or go to classes. Anything goes if it's a useful and positive diversion.

Nursery Fun

Night time comes and lights are out,
The bedroom's quiet and sleep is about,
The toys lie waiting on the shelf so high,
Hours of adventure will make time fly.

The house is quiet so the fun can start,
The toys line up to play their part,
They gather in groups to make the rules
Some sitting on chairs and others on stools.

Said Mr. Bear: "We could take the car",
"No", said Panda, "you couldn't drive that far",
"We could climb a tree", said Winnie the Poo,
"But Snail hates heights so that won't do."

So they then decided to take a bath
And they all lined up on the furry mat,
Those with clothes then took them off,
But one bear wouldn't 'cos he'd got a cough.

Baby Born took charge and said: "Lets go",
With Furby's help she set the water to flow,
Barbie and Ken spread towels on the floor
To keep the bath water from reaching the door.

In they hopped then, one by one,
"We knew", they said, "this would be fun".
They splashed and played amid the froth
Using all the bubble bath the owners bought.

"Shush!", said Balloo, "Don't you dare make noise,
"Conduct yourselves well and keep your poise,
"If we are caught we can never more
Have night time frolics around the floor.

Time sped by and the water went cold,
The night was passing, soon dawn would unfold,
Slowly they climbed right out of the bath,
With whispers and giggles, not daring to laugh.

The small ones returned to the shelf once more,
The older ones tidied the place, as before,
Waving goodbye to the light of the moon,
Planning together for another night soon.

On some of those days during the chemotherapy programme I wasn't able to do all the things I would have liked to do. As time went on I learned to pace myself and be selective in my tasks and, in this way, achieved much more when taken with occasional rest times.

As time went on I became better able to deal with the ups and downs of my new life pattern.

There were days when I'd get a sudden burst of energy and able for a mad cleaning spree.
The following poem has its origins in such a burst of activity. I regularly had to deal with the contradictions of a body telling me to rest and a mind telling me I was getting lazy.
Isn't patience a wonderful virtue for the people who have it?

Professor
Gerry O'Sullivan

Cork Cancer Research Centre

Lisa Crowley, Bernice
& Dr Declan Soden

Lab work

Cork Cancer
RESEARCH CENTRE

Bernice with Scientists
Michelle Nyhan and
Tracey O'Donovan

Mercy University Hospital

Top picture: Professor Gerry O'Sullivan, Director-in-Chief of the Cork Cancer Research Centre, with Bernice and Seán Ó Bulmáin, (Physiotheraphy Department, Mercy University Hospital) at the launch of the Belfast Marathon fund-raiser in 2003 and (below) Bernice and Seán are back to present their cheque. Second from the left is Tony O'Regan, Security Manager at the Mercy University Hospital.

Backache

Oh my God, my back has locked,
I'm done for now and really crocked,
Left of my hip is now very tight,
A stretch or two might put it right.

I gingerly move but to no avail,
I am moving now at the pace of a snail,
My face is drenched in perspiration
And I rub my back in desperation.

I frantically try to carry on,
Then, all of a sudden, the problem is gone,
I've heard a crack and I'm straight once more,
Moving faster, freer than ever before.

I curse and pray with single voice,
I've ground to a halt without a choice,
It's true what they say about your health,
It is truly better than endless wealth.

The most tormenting and persistent questions of the human mind are the speculative what-ifs, if-onlies and the might-have-beens. They are a feature of life and are inevitable as we try to come up with answers to our own trauma and of those we love. That the questions are irrational and worthless is not the point.

Cancer patients and their families are among the best customers of the "What if..?" product. In my own case I spent a lot of time questioning and asking myself if I could have done something to prevent all of this.

One of the ever-patient nurses in the Breast Clinic told me one day that hindsight thoughts and wondering if things could have been different would not change a thing. Nothing of my doing had brought on my cancer.

So, from that day onwards I tried not to look back or to seek answers that were not there.
I tried but I wasn't always successful and there were many occasions when I slipped into my old answer-seeking mode. Eventually, I stopped the questioning altogether and realised there were many people out there much worse off than I.

I had my mobility, my eyesight, my independence, great family and friends and, so, and I tried to move out of the reach of self-pity and recriminations.

What if..?

What if are words I sometimes use,
What if I win? What if I lose?
What if I go? What if I stay?
What if it rains on that special day?

What if I'm late, what should I do?
What if I'm not really liked by you?
What if I fail that important test?
What if my performance isn't the best?

What if my bank account is overdrawn?
What if I sleep out for work, early morn?
What if my family get sick and die?
What if that plane falls out of the sky?

What if the swimming pool water is cold?
What if I've arthritis when I grow old?
What if my home slides down a hole?
What if there's no heaven, worse still no soul?

What if time flies as days go by?
What if while speechmaking I stand up and cry?
"What if?" doesn't help; it may even waste time,
But for all, "What if?" is a pastime of mine.

The poems "Things They Say" and "Funny moments" are from the same fountain of comment and observation by good people who cared and wanted to show their interest and concern.

We are not all in the Diplomatic Service and, even if we were, life would be very boring if every kerbside conversation had to be checked out for political correctness before a word is uttered.

Honest people are wonderful people.

In my case I learned to deal more easily with the questions and comments and stopped taking things personally that knowing people meant well. When I began to see the humour I enjoyed the encounters all the more.

Funny Moments

Bald from chemo, I was window washing,
A neighbour passed by, looking smashing
Commented on my hair piled 'neath a hat,
As I gently told her: "It's not quite like that!"

"In fact, I've none, my hair is gone."
She smiled back thinking I'd led her on
"The chemo took it all", I said.
She drew a breath and then turned red.

Next she asked: "Is your dog inside?"
"No", I told her, "She got sick and died."
The colour drained right through her face
And she wished to be in another place.

Out in a café, having tea,
I saw a person, well known to me,
I called her, asking "how are you?"
But who I was she hadn't a clue.

A caller to my door one sunny morn,
Asked if my clothes were not too warm.
I changed the topic but at his persistence
I gave him the answer without resistance.

He changed his gaze and faced the wall,
I laughed and told him "No problem at all!
"What are you selling anyway?"
"Life insurance", was all he'd say.

A friend called over the other night,
She said: "Your eyes look different, very bright.
You like the sun, you've been out and about?"
We laughed as I told that my eyebrows fell out!

Humour is priceless and it's everywhere,
And all so much better if you're willing to share,
It brightens each moment, whatever the day,
Much better than gloom as you go on your way.

I actually passed by the mirror one night and, for a split second, saw a person I did not know. I did not recognise my own reflection.

I was actually frightened as I tried to remember what I had looked like with hair, with eyebrows and eyelashes. Then I remembered that the Mona Lisa had no eyebrows either and I, too, was able to find a sense of humour and smile at the thought.

Ironically, by sheer coincidence, somebody on the next day gave me a photograph of myself taken about six weeks prior to my cancer diagnosis. When I originally saw the picture I thought of myself as overweight and with traces of grey hairs but with a wonderful tan.

Now, looking in the mirror, I would have given anything to be like the person in the photograph.

During treatment my great ally was the fake tan bottle, a new process for me but which worked wonders for my morale and spirit and gave me a vision of me in the past and me in the future when all this ordeal is over.

Mirror Image

I looked in the bedroom mirror last night,
Suddenly I almost died with fright,
I didn't recognise the person there,
But it was me, without my hair.

I smiled at this person while trying to see
Was this lady really me?
She grinned back, seemed very nice,
I looked again perhaps once or twice.

I saw her head there, bald and round,
As she stared back, without a sound,
I seemed to remember the glint in her eyes,
Was it me there in disguise?

We stared a while and watched time pass,
Silent companions in the shining glass,
Each recalling the person before,
Who, in time, would return once more.

Hair loss is one of the most difficult things to deal with and it is particularly difficult for ladies.

Your life-long identity is gone.

Up to this you had the choice to cut or re-style your hair, to have it long or short. Now, everything is outside of your control and that choice is not yours any more.

I was seeing a different person and I was not sure I liked her. In addition, after the mastectomy I felt as if my body was incomplete.

Eventually, I came to accept that, even though I looked a little bit different, it was still me inside. It was a real identity crisis and I try to describe it in this next poem.

Identity Crisis

I wonder if it's me here any more,
Yet I'm thinking like I did before,
My mind still works but in a different way,
With thoughts of hospital every day.

My body parts are no longer complete,
Some days I lower my head in defeat,
I cannot work; I must stay at home,
At times won't even answer the phone.

My hair is gone and my head is pale,
My eyebrows so thin it makes me wail.
I'm not myself, not a single bit,
And I decide I've become an "it".

Meeting a fellow patient I try to explain,
Would you believe she felt the same?
All at once 'twas a huge relief
To find somebody to share this grief.

Life goes on despite all eventualities and that is highly important in keeping us focused. Routine events can be important diversions at times of crisis.

I wrote the following two poems while waiting for the delivery man to arrive and then after I'd stood back to marvel at the navigating skills of these wonderful people and reflect on the conflict of priorities between the designers of houses and those who design outsize furniture.

Waiting for the Delivery Man

One hour passes, well that's not bad,
Two hours pass, wouldn't it drive you mad?
Every noise that I can hear
Must mean the delivery man is getting near.

Six vans pass, then eight, then nine,
Can't he find this house of mine?
They're all the same, just always late,
Still, when he arrives 'twill be worth the wait.

Three more hours then, on a whim,
I get my phone and contact him.
He's on his way, "fifteen minutes more",
But it takes an hour to reach my door.

I greet him like a long-lost friend,
Even though I'm nearly round the bend;
Ten minutes more and he's gone his way.
I've counted each minute of this long day.

It is extraordinary how at times when we are confronted by major issues, we still have time to fuss and bother about relatively insignificant matters.

But at the end of the day if the major issue that confronts us in life has the effect of putting everything else into perspective then it has its own benefits and we should gladly take them on board.

For my part I certainly have revisited my priorities in life.

The New Couch

The grand new couch arrived today,

I wondered was it here to stay,

It seemed much bigger than the door,

Why didn't I think of that before?

The van man looked and thought it out,

Then pushed a bit and swung about,

One surveyed, walking over and back,

The other then produced a sack.

They lined up the couch and I couldn't look,

Expert hands while my hands shook,

Inch by inch with perfect poise,

And I not daring to make a noise.

I feared the door would fall apart,

Could they hear the thumping of my heart?

Then, suddenly, with ease and grace,

'Twas sitting there in my favourite place.

Woollen hats are wonderful when the cold wind of January takes your breath away or when snowflakes hit your face as you take on a bit of outdoor exercise.

But woollen hats and warmer days are a bad combination as I found out when I was trying to compensate for the protective hair crop that was no longer there.

A big step forward was the bandana but then it could blow off to reveal the new me and that was a big worry.

The next poem was written on the first day I ventured out with the bandana to hide my hairless state.

My Prayer

Will somebody out there tell me please

Could my bandana blow off in the breeze?

Should I knot it tightly on my head

Or try the warm wool hat instead.

What will I do if there's a breeze?

Will my head be warm or will it freeze?

Will people stop to look and stare

Or even see that I've got no hair?

So out I went the crowds to face,

And my loyal bandana stayed in place,

Returning home I could only say:

"Thanks for answering my prayer today."

Traffic jams are among life's most irritating and tension-filled events and are a growing feature of daily life.

But they are also a wonderful time for studying the people around, watching their attitude and compiling imagined profiles on who they might be and what are their priorities in life.

I decided one day that most people sitting there probably had a secret side. After all, I looked perfectly normal, or so I thought. I reckoned that the others could have a story to tell as well.

The Traffic Jam

Sitting in a traffic jam, starting to dream....
I wonder if everybody's what they seem.
Are they feeling well and without a care,
Or do they suffer sitting there.

That lovely hair may not be her own,
Maybe bought, not really grown;
Look at that fellow driving the jeep,
He's so switched off he could be asleep.

Perhaps her nose is a reconstruction,
Her shining teeth a reproduction,
Those lovely nails may be acrylic,
The things they do to look idyllic!

That classy Merc with its hungry tank,
Is it really owned owned by the local bank?
Your man up front on the mobile phone,
Is he checking the state of his housing loan?

Amazing isn't it, the things you'll cop
When traffic comes to a grinding stop!
As traffic starts once more to crawl
I know my worries are really small.

Long before my cancer diagnosis I felt it was important to have a positive outlook on life.

I honestly believed that once my surgery was over that, technically, I had a clean bill of health and that all the two layers of treatment to follow would be part of a scheme to make sure this would be the case.

We spend our lives aware of sickness and its consequences. We are also conscious of the need for good health and, sometimes, we fear that the two will collide with dire consequences.

I am convinced that everything happens for a reason, although we may not realise it at the time.

For me, the months after my surgery made me a stronger person and I found out who I really was. I realised how much I was actually capable of doing and how lucky I was to have a strong outlook.

Things could have been far worse but I constantly focused on what I had. I called up every element of discipline and determination I could find and aimed at using the present to enhance the future.

Positive Thoughts

Two days before chemo I went for a run,

Exhilarated by the breeze and sun,

Problems forgotten, I want to shout

With the sounds of nature all about.

A squawking crow, a bird in song,

Nature's sounds to take me along,

Then a gentle calm comes over me

Admiring the colours of a passing bee.

Some days are for having a little cry,

And this trial, I know, will pass me by,

But today as nature helps me through,

I think I'm strong and my problems few.

Even in times of stress it is important to welcome
and enjoy the fun times that come along and the
real experts at generating fun and honest comment
are children. Childhood innocence is magical.

I wrote The Hamster's Brush after my visitors had
left.

Together we never cease to get a good laugh out
of the moment. For me it is a constant reminder
of some of the best aspects of the cancer journey.

The Hamster's Brush

Three little nieces called in to stay
So we sat outside on this summer's day,
We talked of the past, my sister and I,
Discussing the toys of days gone by.

My bandana on and I felt the heat,
"Take it off", said sister, "give yourself a treat."
On we continued with our laughs and chat
But three little girls put an end to that.

One by one they stood in a row,
Gazing at the auntie they should know,
I said: "My hair is like the hamster's fur,
"It might look spiky but I'm still Ber."

One little girl disappeared inside,
Her sisters still staring, open-eyed,
The first one came back in a rush
Proudly holding the hamster's brush.

What could I do but brush my head,
We laughed when we could have cried instead,
My sister's message that came that night
Asked if my crease was straight and right.

Radiotherapy sessions are often an essential part of cancer treatment. In my case they began three months into my chemotherapy regime and, from then on, they ran in tandem.

It was a daunting course although it only involved fifteen sessions in all. Different people I met had an opinion and I was nervous at first.

But then, like other treatments, it became part of my routine made easy by the fact that I was surrounded by wonderful people, highly skilled at their job and always conscious of my concerns.

At the end of the course radiotherapy was another milestone I had passed and another guarantee of a positive future. It was well worthwhile.

Radiotherapy

I arrive at reception at my appointed time,
I go to the area I now know as mine,
People nod or greet me as I wait,
We are all brought here by a twist of fate.

My card is collected and I'm called in a while,
In my blue paper gown I travel in style,
Next to the specialist, I step into the room,
My radiotherapy session is starting soon.

Measurements and figures checked one by one,
Confirmed by therapists, preparation done,
The area covered with a sheet and a tape,
"It won't be long now", they say as I wait.

The familiar green light starts to show,
Sounds and movements, we're ready to go,
The background's soothing, soft music plays,
But I count out the seconds on each therapy day.

I try not to move, I'm positioned with care
By the wonderful staff who look after me there.
The specialist frequently checks to see
If I'm comfortable as I should be.

Treatment complete, I'm ready to go,
I'll be back again in two days or so,
Plenty fluids, that's what they'll say,
To prevent some problems coming my way.

A natural and warm smile is a sight to behold and many complain that it is disappearing fast from modern life, especially in the shops, public offices, bars and restaurants.

Some people master the art of smiling even when they have little reason to smile. It takes a bit of doing on occasions and in no way is it an outer sign of an insincere heart or mind. Sometimes it hides real personal desperation.

In my case during treatment a particular friend would tune into the tactic if the smile and the moment did not add up. She would say: "Look at the eyes....!"

During my treatment it often took a very special effort to smile and be constantly nice. Now, that my cover is blown, all future smiles are guaranteed to be genuine.

Did you ever get tired of being nice?

Did you ever get tired of being nice?

It's happened to me once or twice,

When I'm smiling a smile with a grin large and wide

But I'm secretly fuming and frothing inside.

I seem all so pleasant, responding so well,

Not one sigh of turmoil, not a sign of a yell,

I answer all questions but I'm dying to say:

"I don't want to talk, at least not today."

It happens but rarely, of that I'm so glad,

I'd hate to find out I'd made someone feel bad;

It's hard to be calm, holding back has a price,

But sometimes I simply get tired of being nice.

I love the heat of the sun and the warm breeze of summer and can barely tolerate the months of cold and rain until May arrives again.

It gives me a sneaking suspicion that I was really meant to be living somewhere else where warmth and calm and the gentle life prevail.

During the months of treatment I made a special effort to keep calm and it was a great help although the inevitable storm clouds were very often too close for comfort.

Little things all around us can help promote an atmosphere that diminishes fear and concern and restores gentle calm and reassurance.

Serenity

All peace and calm, and not a sound,
My dog's gently snoring on the ground,
The sunshine warm upon my face
With wonderful feelings 'round the place.

The sound of a plane that's up in the clouds,
Car horns somewhere, too angry and loud,
In the middle of calmness the telephone rings,
Then back to the peace that this lovely day brings.

Not a single sound of a human voice,
Nature is silent as if by choice,
The sound of water that's running somewhere
Is the only intrusion of which I'm aware.

A wonderful calmness comes over me
This is how I would want it to be,
I close my eyes and gently rest,
It's a heavenly moment with life at its best.

The new pup, a black cocker spaniel, finally arrived in May. I called him William. Perhaps it is not a coincidence that in the early months of treatment when I couldn't sleep, I would often focus on a spaniel's looks and use the vision to help me to sleep.

The arrival of such an energetic but totally affectionate and intelligent pup was one of the best decisions I made. He helped to divert my mind away from hospitals and drugs and appointments.

Unfortunately, as inquisitive puppies do, he was over-interested in my long hairpiece. Like many humans he was in shock the first time he saw me without it and stopped dead on his tracks believing he was looking at a different person.

His puppy brain worked overtime on occasions trying to figure out why part of my head was drying over a vase. The next little poem is a tribute to the new dog and his timely arrival at my house.

The New Pup

Boundless energy and endless fun,
He never walks but always runs;
He chews the rug and bites the chair,
Where will it end, I ask in despair.

He cries like a baby, he loves me so,
He's sniffing and scurrying to and fro,
His puppy habits will change, they say,
But his puppy ways won't all go away.

He chases that ball with breakneck speed,
Floppy ears flapping, a sign of his breed,
Nothing is safe, better cover your toes,
Watch your fingers and mind your nose.

I just love him, what else can I say?
I enjoy him more with each passing day,
He thrills and torments but you must agree
That I'd simply be lost if he ran out on me.

I will be eternally grateful to my family and my friends who were loyal and caring but always giving me the space to lead my own life and fight my battles in my own way.

I am fortunate to have three sisters who are very special. Writing and re-reading this poem I wondered, and still wonder, how they managed to combine minding their children, keeping their jobs and still making contact with me on a daily basis as well as making regular visits. It went on over the weeks and months since the first diagnosis ten months ago back in November. They took my sickness and pain as if it had been their own.

Some might say that that's just what good sisters do. It is still an exceptional act of love and giving and my poem is a tribute, too, to all loving, caring sisters and brothers of women and men who go through the cancer journey.

In Praise of Sisters

Three lovely sisters whom I adore,
No one could ask for a single gift more,
In moments of stress they all come up trumps,
Supporting and helping when I'm in the dumps.

It's a wonderful thing that they know every day,
If it's right for a visit or to just stay away;
They would quietly phone and would never intrude,
But would ask if today they could lighten my mood.

Time passes by and the treatment goes on,
Their kindness unending as I journey on,
The constant showing of how they care,
Is the wonderful gift that sisters share.

Of course I get cross and in terrible form
But they treat it as if it's all part of the norm,
No job is too big regardless of time,
For these wonderful, caring sweet sisters of mine.

Three lovely sisters whom I adore,
No one could ask for a single gift more,
In moments of stress they all come up trumps,
Supporting and helping when I'm in the dumps.

This poem honours mothers.

I think of my own mother, of her love, wisdom and calm, constant support.

I think of all the mothers I met over the months and who juggled difficult treatments and day-to-day events like appointments and making plans in an attempt to maintain stability and normality in the daily lives of their families back at home.

I remember the stories of triumph and achievement, of family joys, of matches played, birthday parties that went ahead and of all the occasions so special in a child's life.

They were wonderful people and typical of all mothers for whom the well-being and happiness of family is never forgotten as they pursue their own personal battle to return to full health.

The Mother

A mother's the solid backbone of the group,
The leader and organiser of the troupe,
Co-ordinator and planner if things start going wrong,
The soother of troubles who'll guide you along.

With calmness a mother keeps the show on the road,
She's the willing bearer of everyone's load,
The solver of problems with a gift for advice,
From morning to night she's unfailingly nice.

The mother is understanding and well organised,
She's the one with solutions for all sorts of trials,
She can come up with answers when answers are few,
With the wisdom of years she will know what to do.

A mother's job list is endless, her energy vast,
She never stops going so how does she last?
Of this I am sure, if Rome was built in a day,
'Twas the mothers who did it, there was no other way.

One of the worst things that can happen during cancer treatment is to discover that your chemo has to be postponed due, perhaps, to the fact that your blood test has shown the white cell count to be too low.

I felt utterly devastated and personally responsible whenever it happened. One couldn't really describe the disappointment on such days.

It was, of course, absolutely wise of the superb oncology staff to withhold treatment on days like this. But they were often privy to my unsavoury reaction when it happened and we got many a good laugh at the next visit when treatment went ahead.

Days of Curses and Swears

Each time I fear the nurse will just say,
"We're not able to give you the chemo today"
Another week's waiting, endless days, troubled nights,
I must wait a bit more 'til the white cells are right.

I smile and I thank her, not showing my eyes,
I know she is right and the week's wait is wise,
But my huge disappointment I cannot express,
Or tell of my feelings of loss and distress.

I pick up my bag and I head for the door,
The staff are all wonderful, they've seen it before,
But once I'm outside and there's nobody there
Its my time to let fly with the curses and swears.

Once you get into the routine of chemotherapy it is habit-forming and, in a strange way, becomes almost a social occasion.

My visits became an essential part of my life for medical reasons but a special bond invariably develops between patient and staff and between patient and patient.

Naturally, the joy of ending treatment and the feelings of achievement on the final day were overwhelming.

In retrospect it was a major learning experience. I remember, before I started chemo, I asked if I could see the area where it all took place. I remember to this day the shock on realising that I would be in there, a part of it all. Me getting chemo!

In reality it became natural and undaunting and was just a matter of meeting good friend for a few hours at regular intervals. It was just another day at the office.

The Office

I must go to the 'office' today,
It's Wednesday and I can't delay,
I pack my bag and away I go
To the Oncology Unit I've come to know.

Wonderful nurses will warmly greet
By name each patient that they meet,
Treating us all to the kind of smile
That almost makes the day worthwhile.

Blood counts checked and lines in site,
The tea arrives to my great delight,
Comfy chairs and friendly staff,
And, believe it or not, the occasional laugh.

Drugs selected by this masterly team,
Each patient following a set regime,
Constantly checking without a fuss,
The nurses take absolute care of us.

Then when the treatment is complete,
I quickly hop up and back on my feet,
Glad that the morning finally ends
"Bye 'til next week" to my newfound friends.

This poem was written a while back to show appreciation for true friendship.

Real friends accept you as you are. They ask for nothing but give so much. You never feel you have to owe them. There is no charge or demand. Everything is unconditional.

Their sense of constant giving is only matched by their desire to be consulted and asked to advise and help yet again.

For me, I appreciate more than words could say, the gift of true friends.

My only wish is that I, in return, could be to them what they have been to me, not just for today or tomorrow but for life. My chance may come. One such friend was diagnosed with cancer and took on The Journey I had just completed.

The Friend

Diamonds are a girl's best friend, they say,
But it should be phrased the other way,
Man's best friend is a diamond bright,
A wonderful person, a shining light.

The friend is the one who will always care,
The one who is always there to share,
They help you through the difficult day,
And you know they'll never be too far away.

True friends ignore your darker days,
And gently bring you to happier ways,
They urge you on to meet that test,
Assuring you that you're the best.

They'd believe in you, no matter what,
They'd remember occasions that others forgot,
They inspire you more than words can say,
You appreciate their friendship every day.

Long before I had any cancer diagnosis I was already a keen fund-raiser for the Cork Cancer Research Centre and the work it undertakes to find vital answers to benefit the present and future generations.

Family members and friends had developed cancer. Some had survived, some had not.

I worked in an Intensive Care Unit where I saw at first hand the devastation of families and the trauma for patients with cancer.

I was aware at close range of the work being done at the Mercy University Hospital and at University College College Cork by Professor Gerry O'Sullivan and his wonderful team. I was already deeply aware that research was the key to future success.

Much progress has been made. The drugs and cancer management techniques used today are the result of improved research.
Here in Cork we have ongoing specific and very intensive research by the Cork Cancer Research Centre at the Mercy University Hospital and at UCC. But research by its nature is extremely costly and the work is very much under-funded.

I want to use this book to honour the work and to stress how it can be helped along by sustained public goodwill and commitment as well as fund-raising of all kinds.

Answers will be found. Let us speed up that moment.

Cancer Research

Never let research be under-rated,
It's importance should always be clearly stated,
Researchers are seeking a permanent cure
For the awful traumas that people endure.

Education is great and prevention a feat,
And modern medicine has new ways to treat,
Early detection gives the very best chance,
But it's research that pinpoints the way to advance.
                    .

Through research, all cancer statistics will fall,
The benefits, long-term, will reach out to all,
Cancer diagnoses will no longer dismay
And the "Big C" phobia will then go away.

When in the future the answer is reached,
The benefits to all can then be preached,
The world will become a brighter place,
And people on earth a healthier race.

Facing the Challenge

So, as we near the end of this little book, you might ask me what it is that keeps you going from diagnosis to end of treatment without looking back.

My views and beliefs are mine alone and other people have their own strengths and outlooks.

As I see it, it has to come from within the patient. Family and friends are vital and the hospital care and the excellent highly-trained and well-practiced professionals are critical to your success. But what I call The Journey is made by the patient

I would, with great humility, say this to anybody who is given a cancer diagnosis:

You are a good and strong person.

You won't waste time with recriminations and asking "Why Me?" or "What If?"

You have things to do, a challenge ahead.

You are well up to the challenge.

You will have the best professional help to see you through.

You will travel The Journey one day at a time.

You are determined to win.

You will triumph and feel all the better as a person because of your courage and belief in yourself.

Go for it and don't look back!

The Door to New Beginning

It's 13.45, on Tuesday the 15th. of August, 2006. It's a very special day in my life when I move forward from what has been and resume the challenges of a regular and normal life.

It occurs to me that doors offer us all three options. We have the option of stepping forward, stepping backwards or staying right where we are and doing nothing.

I am standing here with my back to the Oncology Department door. I have just completed my final chemotheraphy session. Several months ago I elected to walk through the door and take on the challenges of cancer surgery and cancer treatment. Today I feel good about myself. The sky overhead is dismal and cloudy and the wonderful summer may have ended. But, for me, the sun is still shining.

I have challenged my fears and I've come through. The journey is over. I've completed the circle.

My humble wish is that my poems and stories and the little bits of personal philosophy that accompany them would encourage other people who are forced to stand in the doorway on Decision Day to have the courage to step inside that door, to take on the challenges and, in time, feel the joy and freedom and sense of achievement of coming out again into the sunshine of a new life.

- BERNICE